Plays f
Social Impact

A Wee Taste

Patricia Byrne

A Sole Purpose Publication

First published in September 2018.

Copyright © 2018 Patricia Byrne/Sole Purpose Productions

Sole Purpose Productions
5-7 Artillery Street
Derry-Londonderry BT48 6RG
T: 0044 (0) 28 7127 9918
E: solepurpose@mac.com
W: www.solepurpose.org
Facebook: Sole Purpose Productions
Twitter: @SolePurpose_

The right of Patricia Byrne to be identified as the author of this work has been
asserted in accordance with the Copyright, Designs and Patents Act 1988.

Original poster design for *A Wee Taste* by Kieran Ferris.

Photographs: Copyright © Max Beer

Layout and design: Hive Studios: www.hivestudio.org; T: (028) 7127-7487

A CIP catalogue record for this book is available from the British Library.

ISBN 978-1-9164453-2-1

This publication is funded
by the Halifax Foundation
for Northern Ireland.

Sole Purpose Productions
is core funded by the Arts
Council of Northern Ireland.

Introduction

A Wee Taste was written to raise awareness of the issue of underage drinking. It was developed through interviews and research with the Northlands Centre, the Drink Think Project and the Divert Project. The aims of this production were to: deglamorise alcohol; raise awareness of the personal dangers of the effects of alcohol; explore the emotional and psychological effects of the overuse of alcohol such as low self-esteem and depression; look at loss of motivation, loss of talents and the negative effects on schoolwork; consider the drinking habits of parents and the effects on young people.

The characters in the play are Jenni, a 14-year-old, and her mother, Kate, who likes a drink. We watch the dynamics between them as Jenni's drinking increases and her mother feels powerless to do anything about it. The play toured to 15 venues across Ireland. Each performance was followed by a Q&A with the actors in character. Follow-up workshops entitled 'Counting the Cost of Alcohol', co-ordinated by Community Direct and facilitated by Debbie Caulfield, took place in the schools a couple of weeks after the performances. These workshops explored the physical effects of alcohol on the body and the brain; the consequences of getting a criminal record; the recommended limits for drinking and keeping safe; looking at change and breaking habits.

This was a very successful tour. The production reached over 2,500 young people, teachers, carers, parents, social workers and general public. The production served as an intervention tool to raise awareness among young people of the negative impacts of underage drinking. The follow-up 'Counting the Cost of Alcohol' workshops were a very important aspect of the project. These gave very practical information on the misuse of alcohol and keeping safe.

During the tour we received requests to do performances for parents. In 2012 we staged extra performances for parents and carers. Parental drinking habits are an important aspect of the misuse of alcohol among young people and an issue that is explored in the play. Many parents reported that the play made them reflect on their own drinking habits and the impacts on their children.

The production was funded by Derry City Council, Derry Community Safety Partnership and the Drinkaware Trust.

5

Acknowledgements

Thank you to First Call Drama Group for their feedback and suggestions for the script. Many thanks to Roisin Richmond, Christina McClements, Joanne Smith and Debbie Caulfield for assistance with script development. A heartfelt thank you to Shauna Kelpie who supported me in bringing this production to life, and many others.

I am deeply grateful to the Board of Directors of Sole Purpose Productions for their support and guidance throughout this process.

Production Details

A Wee Taste was first produced by Sole Purpose Productions and performed at The Derry Playhouse on 9 November 2011. The Director was Shauna Kelpie, the cast were Gemma Walker (Jenni) and Carmel McCafferty (Kate). It was produced by Patricia Byrne. Lighting and Sound Design was by Martin McDonald, Costume Design was by Helen Quigley. The Stage Manager was Debbie Caulfield, assisted by Alex Wilson.

Reviews/Testimonies

'*A Wee Taste* is an engrossing and compelling play. I noticed that all the young people around me were engrossed too – quite an achievement! Gemma Walker and Carmel McCafferty were brilliant, the script flowed really well. Congratulations!'
Christina McClements, Counsellor,
Northlands Addiction Treatment Centre, Derry

'We had a large audience comprising young people, parents, youth workers, PSNI Diversionary Officers and social workers. It is a very hard-hitting play addressing key messages about the consequences of underage drinking. The actors' engagement with the audience was excellent.'
Leona McGee, Project Officer,
Fermanagh Community Safety Partnership

'An outstanding performance which was thoroughly enjoyed by all in the audience. The script and performance struck home with the pupils in a way that was entertaining, educational and above all believable. Schools need more work of this quality!'
Damien Clarke, Pastoral Co-ordinator,
St Patrick's College, Maghera

Dedicated to our young people.

Stay safe. Be happy.

SET
Kitchen with a kitchen table, two chairs, cupboards. JENNI's bedroom with a bed and bedside table, messy. Minimal set.

CHARACTERS
JENNI – 14-year-old girl, the actor also plays other incidental characters.

KATE, JENNI's mother, early 50s

SCENE 1

KATE in the kitchen. JENNI offstage.

JENNI: Ma! Ma! *(From offstage.)*

KATE: Yes, I'm here.

Enter JENNI.

JENNI: Ma! I got an A+ in my Art test. The teacher said I am the best in the class! She said she thinks I could be a very good artist.

KATE: That's great, love. Do you know what jobs you can get with Art?

JENNI: Ma, I just like Art. You're always on about jobs. Can I go to a birthday party next week? I got invited by this girl.

KATE: Who?

JENNI: Sophie.

KATE: I never heard you mention her before. Where does she live?

JENNI: I dunno, Ma, why do you always ask so many questions?

KATE: Maybe I'm getting more like you. If you're going to her birthday party then you need to know where it is.

JENNI: It's not her birthday party, it's her friends. Anyway, I'll find that out.

KATE: It would be useful, wouldn't it? Is Jacob going?

JENNI: I don't know. Why do you want to know if Jacob's going?

KATE: Because he is sensible, I know he'll keep an eye out for you.

JENNI: Jacob's boring.

KATE: I'll put the dinner on. You go and do some homework now.

JENNI: Can I go to the party?

KATE: We'll see. Go and do your homework.

JENNI: What? Now? Can't I watch TV?

KATE: Homework first. TV later. Go on.

JENNI: I haven't got that much to do. I'll do it later.

KATE: If you haven't got much to do, then get it done now and it'll be finished. Go on!

JENNI takes her schoolbag, huffy, exit.

KATE to audience.
Everything's a battle! Anything I say she has an answer for, another question, another battle. It wears me out. I've brought up teenagers before, you'd think I'd know how to do it. But I'm older now. Jenni came along late. We were shocked, not expecting it at all. Then, out of nowhere, there's a baby on the way! But she was a beautiful baby, and so good! Slept through the night from really early on and was never any trouble. A wee angel. She's got very headstrong lately, answers back a lot. Her father and I separated a few years ago. She took it hard. She's got more moody since then.

JENNI enters bedroom.

JENNI to audience.
Oh I hope Mammy lets me go to that party. They're always talking in school about going out and what they did the night before. They have great craic. They drink. I haven't been out drinking yet. Well I've had a bit, but just at home, if Mammy lets me have something when she's got

friends round. The ones in school all hang out together. Sophie told me that they were all drinking in the park the other night, there was about 20 of them. She said they were all messing about and dancing, they had music and all, it was like a proper rave. I wish I'd been there.

Shouting from one room to the other.

JENNI: Ma!

KATE: What!

JENNI: Can I go to that party?

KATE: I said we'll see.

JENNI: That mean's yes, sweet!

KATE: No, it means I'll think about it.

JENNI: Please! Everyone else is going.

KATE: Get your homework done and we'll talk about it.

JENNI: Yeah! Thank you, Mammy, you're the best mammy ever!

KATE exit.

SCENE 2

JENNI's bedroom. JENNI getting ready for the party. Music playing. JENNI singing to a pop song, pretending to be a singer. Putting party clothes on, make up, putting hair up.

JENNI to audience.
The party is tonight! Ooooh! I hope Rory will be there. I really like him. He talks to me. He said he likes my hair. One day in school I was doing

some work and I saw him looking at me, just looking. And I got this excited feeling in me, it went right through me, it was all warm and nice. He does Art too, he's really good. I wonder what he would like on me.

Holding different tops up against her, pretending to talk to Rory.

Hi, Rory, didn't know you were going to be here. Hey, you look really good. I like your top, Rory, where did you get that? Oh my God, you don't say that to a boy, do you? You like my hair? *(Shaking her head.)* Thanks. I like your... your... eyes, face, hands, body... everything! Let's dance.

She pretends she is dancing with him. He moves closer. She pretends he is kissing her.

Oh, Rory, you're such a good kisser!

She giggles.

I want him to be my boyfriend, and we can go out together, we can go to the pictures, for burgers, go bowling, swimming. Oh, that would be soooo sweet.

I'm meeting Sophie at the corner shop on her road, then we'll meet the others and go to the party. Ma said she would take me but no-one else's mas are dropping them off, so I can't let my ma do that. I can just hear everybody: 'Jenni's ma left her off, like a baby, baby Jenni, baby Jenni.'

She finishes getting ready. Goes out singing and dancing.

Let's party!

SCENE 3

The actor playing Jenni also plays the parts of Sophie and Jacob.

At the party, loud music, JENNI is dancing.

The party's great! Loads of people. The parents have a really big house, so we have a whole section all to ourselves. Sophie gets me something to drink. It's blue.

JENNI: What is it?

SOPHIE: Just drink it, you'll like it.

JENNI: It tastes like sweets.

SOPHIE: Yeah, great isn't it? You'll get monkeyed really quick on that.

JENNI: What's it like being monkeyed?

SOPHIE: It's sweet. You feel so good. You can talk to anybody, you don't feel shy, it's really good craic.

JENNI to audience.
Me and Sophie drink alcopops. There's loads of drinks here. I tried a bit of everything. Jacob's here. I've known him since I was four. He lives down our street. He's older than me.

JACOB: What are you doing here?

JENNI: I'm with Sophie.

JACOB: Sophie?

JENNI: From school. *(Offering Jacob a drink.)* You want some?'

JACOB: No. I don't drink.

JENNI: You don't drink? Why not?

JACOB: I don't like it.

JENNI: How can you not like it?

JACOB: Just don't. See you later.

JENNI to audience.
And he goes off with his mates. I'm loving this party, I'm having such a great time, I can talk to everyone. I can dance when I want to and don't feel shy. And guess what! Guess who's walking this way! Rory, OMG, he looks soooo gorgeous.

JENNI: Hi, Rory! I didn't know you were coming! Yeah, I'm having a great time. When did you get here? Oh just about 20 minutes ago. Where were you? Round a mate's? What? Do I want to dance? Yeah!

She is dancing but is a bit drunk, falling about a bit.

SCENE 4

KATE sitting with glass of wine. JENNI tries to go in without being seen.

KATE: Hello, Jenni, you got back ok then. Did your friend's mother pick you up?

JENNI: Yep.

KATE: You're late. Did you get my texts?

JENNI: No. I didn't have any credit.

KATE: How was the party?

JENNI: It was good.

KATE: Were there many there?

JENNI: Yeah, loads… I'm going to bed.

KATE: Ok, goodnight. Sleep well.

JENNI: Night!

JENNI goes to the bedroom.

SCENE 5

Bedroom. JENNI to audience.
Ohhh! I am so dying. Everything's spinning. Ohhh! Feel sick. Ohhh! But what a great time I had. It was great being with everyone, I wasn't feeling shy, I could say anything and it was alright! I was funny! And I could talk to boys! Rory danced with me. He is so nice. Sophie's going out on Friday and asked me to come. A friend of her's parents are going away, and we're all going round. I can't wait. I hope Rory is there again. Ohhhh, FML, I'm dying.

She trips and knocks something over. Mother from kitchen.

KATE: Are you alright?

JENNI: Yeah.

JENNI exit.

SCENE 6

Kitchen, JENNI coming home from school.

KATE: Hello, love. How did you get on today?

JENNI: Ok.

KATE: How was that maths test?

JENNI: Ok.

KATE: You alright?

JENNI: Yeah, just tired. Sophie's invited me over to stay on Friday night, can I go?

KATE: A sleepover? To stay overnight?

JENNI: Yeah.

KATE: Why do you need to stay overnight?

JENNI: We're just going to hang out. It'll be really good. Please.

KATE: Well can't you just hang out and then come home?

JENNI: No, it's just really good to stay over.

KATE: Will her mum and dad be there?

JENNI: Yeah, they will.

KATE: Ok then. Friday?

JENNI: Aye.

KATE: What time do you want to go?

JENNI: About seven.

KATE: Ok. Maybe I'll have a night out then.

JENNI: Yeah, you should. I'll go and do some homework.

KATE: Great. Dinner will be ready soon.

JENNI goes to leave, then comes back.

JENNI: Ma.

KATE: Yes.

JENNI: Can I have some money?

KATE: What do you want money for?

JENNI: I owe some to Sophie.

KATE: What for?

JENNI: Last week, when we went shopping, she loaned me some money for a top I wanted to buy, I didn't have enough.

KATE: What top? I didn't see any new top.

JENNI: Er... I left it at Sophie's.

KATE: How much was it?

JENNI: £25.

KATE: £25! I'm not giving you £25!

JENNI: No, she loaned me £10. The top was £25.

KATE: So you want £10?

JENNI: Yes.

KATE: Ok then, but I want to see this top.

JENNI: Thanks, Ma.

JENNI goes to bedroom. KATE exit.

SCENE 7

Bedroom. JENNI phones Sophie on mobile phone.
JENNI: Hi, Sophie. Me ma said I can go. I told her I was staying over at your house. Did you ask your ma yet?... Sweet. I can't wait till Friday. It's gonna be so good. Is Rory going? Yeah! What you gonna wear?... I dunno yet. Yeah, I got some money so we can get some drink. Do you think Rory likes me?... Yeah?... What did he say?... Really? Oh, I like him so much. Yeah, see you in school tomorrow. Bye.

SCENE 8

JENNI moves stage front, talks to audience.
It's Friday night, we're up the back lane. There's loads of us. Everyone is drinking. I feel a bit nervous. I don't like what I'm wearing. I think it looks lame. Sophie has got the drinks. She knows someone older who got them for us. I take one of those blue drinks I like. After a couple I'm feeling better, more relaxed. I'm talking to them, I'm laughing, it's ok. I see Rory talking to some of the others. Sophie calls him over. She's so confident. He's got vodka... 'Aye, I'll have some.'... I take it, I drink it, mix it with the blue drink. We're talking and laughing, I like it. I'm laughing louder. Sophie goes off and talks to other people she knows. Rory gets closer... 'Here, have more vodka.' Don't think I should, feeling a bit dizzy. 'Go on, have some more. Don't be a lightweight.' I don't want to be a lightweight. I take some more. Yeah, it's good. He puts his arm around me. I feel his body against mine. He starts kissing my neck, it feels nice, but I don't feel well. He takes me into a corner. I feel his hands on me, under my clothes... everything gets blurred.

She falls to the ground.

I don't remember, I don't remember much. Rory was there. I wake up in Sophie's house. Sophie, what happened last night? I don't remember. I feel sick. Where's the toilet?

Exit.

SCENE 9

Kitchen. Mother enters. Tottering on high heels, singing.

Oh what a night, late December back in '63, was a very special night for me, late December, what a night... (Humming to herself.)

Kate to audience.
It was seventies night down the bar. Great to get out! I danced all night! *(Dancing round the kitchen table, singing.) Oh what a night! Da da da da da da...*

She trips and sits down. Oh, oh dear, ooooh dear...

Not so steady on my feet now. Ohhhh, head spinning a bit. I saw Rosie and Mandy and Mary and... what's her name?... oh can't think of it now. Was great to see them all. A good night out, just what I needed. Don't get out much now since the separation. Didn't get out that much before, but at least I had company. Nothing now. No-one at home. I miss him. Yeah... miss him. Or maybe it's not him I actually miss, maybe it's just having someone around, you know?

Jenni's growing up now, she'll be gone soon. Doing her own thing. Then it really will be an empty house. *(Pause. Her head in her hands.)* Oh well, you've just got to keep going, haven't you, eh? Yep, just keep going. Oooooh God, my head. Shouldn't have had that last brandy. *(She gets up.)* Time for the toilet. *(She staggers off.)*

SCENE 10

Bedroom. Next day after school, in school uniform. JENNI is texting on the phone. We see her texting for a while.

JENNI to audience.
Oh no! How did this happen! Shite! There's a photo of me with Rory the other night. My top is pulled up, showing my... *(Indicates her breasts.)* He's laughing, pointing at me. Sophie says it's going all around the

21

school. How can I go to school tomorrow? Everyone'll be looking at me, laughing at me. I'm not going, I'm not going to school tomorrow.

KATE enters kitchen.

KATE: Jenni! Dinner's ready.

JENNI: I'm not hungry. I don't want anything!

KATE: C'mon you've got to eat something.

JENNI: No, I don't want anything.

KATE goes into bedroom.

KATE: Are you alright?

JENNI: Yeah, no… I don't feel well.

KATE: What's wrong?

JENNI: I've got stomach ache.

KATE: Do you feel sick?

JENNI: Yeah.

KATE: Do you feel like you want to get sick?

JENNI: Yeah, a bit.

KATE: What did you eat today?

JENNI: Just lunch at school, that's all.

KATE: Do you have a temperature? *(Feels her forehead.)*

JENNI: I dunno.

KATE: You feel a bit warm. Do you want a drink of water?

JENNI: No, I just want to sleep.

KATE: You sure?

JENNI: Yes.

KATE: Ok then, I'll let you rest for a bit.

KATE exit. JENNI gets her laptop and opens it up.

JENNI: OMG! There's photos all over Facebook! FML! Hundreds of people are going to see this. The whole town will know! The names they're calling me. Slag? I'm not a slag! I didn't even know he was doing this! I'll never be able to face anyone again.

Exit.

SCENE 11

JENNI and KATE in the kitchen.

KATE: Jenni, you've been off school for a couple of days now. I can't take any more time off work. And you won't go to the doctor. You have to go to school. I don't think there's anything wrong with you.

JENNI: Ma, I can't go, I'm not well.

KATE: You have to go to the doctor then. Or shall I call him?

JENNI: No.

KATE: Well, you have to go to school. Is something else wrong? Has something happened at school?

JENNI: No.

KATE: Well, you've got no excuses.

JENNI: Ok, ok, I'll go!

KATE's phone rings.

KATE: Yes, hello. Yes, that's me. *(Pause)* Jenni hasn't been well… *(Pause)* No, I didn't know about that. Yes, she will be in tomorrow. Thank you for letting me know, goodbye.

KATE looks at JENNI.

KATE: That was the school.

JENNI: Was it?

KATE: A photo of you was found on a boy's phone, it was passed around the school.

JENNI is quiet.

KATE: Is that what this is all about? Is that why you don't want to go to school?

JENNI is quiet.

KATE: Well the boy has been suspended from school. His phone has been taken off of him. Jacob reported him.

JENNI: Jacob did?

KATE: Yes, he did the right thing. That boy's name could go on the Sex Offenders Register for this. That means that jobs he applies for can get that information about him. How did that boy get that photo of you?

JENNI is quiet.

KATE: Jenni, were you drinking?

JENNI nods.

KATE: Where were you drinking?

JENNI: Up the lane.

KATE: Where did the drink come from?

JENNI: Someone got it for us.

KATE: And what happened?

JENNI: This boy was trying to kiss me.

KATE: What boy?

JENNI: Just a boy that was there.

KATE: Jenni, you are far too young to be drinking! And far too young to be kissing boys! You are not going out after this.

JENNI: But, Ma, it was only…

KATE: No, Jenni! You're not going out! And you are going to school tomorrow!

JENNI: Yes, ok!

JENNI exit. KATE pours a glass of wine. She is frustrated and angry. She sees JENNI's phone on the table. She picks it up and starts looking at the texts. She exits with the wine and the phone.

SCENE 12

JENNI in bedroom, next day. JENNI to audience.
School was shite! I hate school! I saw other kids looking at me. I know they were all talking about me. Even Sophie was funny with me, well,

at first she was. I saw Rory at lunchtime outside school, in the distance. He didn't see me, or pretended he didn't see me. I don't care. I don't like him anymore anyway. I'm glad he got into trouble. Sophie came over to me later. She brought a couple of those alcopops in the little cartons. She gave me some. I felt a bit better after that. It didn't matter so much that everyone was looking at me. I didn't care anymore. They're going out tonight, I'm going too.

JENNI gets changed. She walks through kitchen to go out. KATE is in the kitchen.

JENNI: Bye, Ma.

KATE: Where are you going?

JENNI: I'm going to Sophie's.

KATE: I said you can't go out.

JENNI: I'm only going to Sophie's.

KATE: It's a school night. You can't go out on a school night. Have you done your homework?

JENNI: I didn't get any homework. I'll be back early.

KATE: Jenni, you can't go out. You haven't asked me.

JENNI: I don't need to ask you. I'm not a kid anymore.

KATE: Oh yes you are!

JENNI: Ma, you can't stop me from going out. I'll see you later.

KATE: What time will you be back?

JENNI: Dunno.

JENNI exit.

KATE: Jenni! You come back here! What! I don't believe that! Who does she think she is! Talking to me like that!

KATE exit.

SCENE 13

JENNI to audience.
We're up the alley. There's a massive crowd of us, there must be about 50. I'm cold. I didn't bring a jacket with me. I'm trying to get drunk quickly so that I don't care anymore about what the others think of me. Sophie has started smoking. They're passing it around.

SOPHIE: You want some?

JENNI: What's it like?

SOPHIE: Amazing. Go on, have a pull on it.

JENNI takes a pull, she coughs. To audience.
Er… it burns my throat. I take another pull on it. I start to feel lightheaded, I start shaking, but I keep going. I don't want them to think I can't do it. It's ok after a while but it tastes horrible.

Rory comes over. He starts joking around. I hate him. He puts his arm around me.

JENNI: Get off me!

She pushes him away. Actor plays both parts.

RORY: What's wrong, you not up for it tonight?

JENNI: I wasn't 'up for it' the other night!

RORY: Didn't look like it to me.

JENNI: What did you put that photo around school for?

RORY: Just a bit of fun. Can't you take a joke?

JENNI: It wasn't fun for me!

RORY: You're just a prude, you're frigid.

JENNI: I'm glad you got into trouble for it.

RORY: I'm gonna get him, that weirdo. He's a grass. *(He walks away.)* You wait and see!

JENNI to audience.
I need more drink. Some boys are climbing a tree. They're really high up. Everyone's cheering them on. *(She cheers.)* Go on! Go on! Higher! Higher! Higher! They're really high up. Climbing up through the branches. *(She cheers again.)* One of them has slipped. It looks like a part of the tree has broken. He's hanging there. It breaks some more. He comes falling down. He lands with a great thud. Nobody moves. He's just lying there. Some kids rush to him. He's not moving. They try to wake him. His eyes are closed. OMG everybody's panicking.

Then he jumps up and shouts, 'Got ye!' He's alright! Some fellas are pushing him about and having the craic. They start fighting, just messing. Rory is pushing one of the lads about. Jacob is standing watching. Rory sees him and goes over to him. He starts pushing him, he is saying something to him, but I can't hear it. Some other boys join in, now they're hitting Jacob. Oh my God, they've got him on the ground and are kicking him. 'Jacob! Jacob!' I go over, but what can I do? There's lights coming towards us. Torches. When they get closer we realise it's the police. Some people run off in different directions. Others are too drunk to do anything. Jacob is on the ground but he gets up. A policewoman comes over to us. 'What's going on here?'... 'They were kicking him,' I say. 'Nothing,' says Jacob. 'It's alright.' He's got blood on his face.

'Are you alright?' the policewoman says. 'Yeah, yeah.' They ask us our names and where we live, and they take us and Sophie home.

Exit.

SCENE 14

KATE (*Talking at the door.*): Thank you, officer. Thank you. Yes, I will keep an eye on her in future.

KATE: What do you think you are doing? Being brought home by the police! Did you hear what she said? She said that you will be reported to the Youth Diversionary Officer. What's everyone going to say? I've been up half the night waiting for you! You didn't answer any of my texts, and don't tell me you had no credit 'cos I know you did! What were you doing drinking in that alley?

JENNI: Just havin' the craic. It's none of your business anyway.

KATE: It is my business. I'm your mother. It is my business to know where you are all the time!

JENNI: I'm not a kid anymore. I can do what I like.

KATE: No you can't! You're drunk.

JENNI: So are you!

KATE: I am not. I've only had a couple of glasses of wine. Anyway, I'm an adult, I can drink what I like.

JENNI: I can drink what I like too.

KATE: You're 14 years of age! You're just a child! You shouldn't be drinking at all!

JENNI: I'm growing up! Everybody drinks!

KATE: You are not grown up yet. And just because everybody else does something it doesn't mean that you have to do the same thing!

JENNI: Oh shut up, you don't know what you're talking about!

KATE: How dare you talk to me like that. You get to bed now. We'll talk about this in the morning.

JENNI: I'm not going to talk about it in the morning. I don't want to talk to you. I hate you. You made Daddy go away with all your moaning. I hate you!

KATE: You go to bed right now! You're not allowed out after this.

JENNI: I'm going. Don't you worry.

JENNI storms off, tearful.

KATE *(Tearful)*: I don't know what to do anymore. She's out of control. I really, really don't know what to do.

Exit.

SCENE 15

KATE enters with a letter in her hand. She opens it and reads it. She looks worried.

KATE: Jenni!

Silence.

KATE: Jenni!

JENNI: What? I'm in the bathroom!

KATE: You're going to be late for school. Get a move on.

JENNI: Ok!

KATE looks at the letter again. JENNI enters.

JENNI: Alright?

KATE: No, I am not alright. That was a disgrace last night.

JENNI: Oh, don't start, Ma.

KATE: This letter just arrived.

JENNI: What is it?

KATE: It's from the school. There's a parents' evening coming up. Your teacher says that she is concerned about your schoolwork, you have been slacking recently and you have tests coming up. She says it is important that we go to the parents' evening.

JENNI: Yeah?

KATE: Yeah.

Silence.

KATE: Is that all you've got to say? Yeah?

JENNI: Yeah. What do you want me to say?

KATE: Why is your schoolwork slacking?

JENNI: I dunno. It's boring. I hate school.

KATE: You used to like school. You used to love Art.

JENNI: Yeah well, like you said, what kind of job could I get with Art?

KATE: You won't get any kind of job if you don't pass any of your exams.

JENNI: Chill out, Ma, I'll pass them ok. There's no jobs anyway, so everyone keeps saying.

KATE: That doesn't matter, you still have to make the effort and pass some exams. Anyway, we'll see what your teacher says at the parents' evening. Now go and get dressed and get to school.

JENNI exit. KATE looks at the letter again.

KATE: Where has my beautiful, sweet, young girl gone?

Exit.

SCENE 16

JENNI in the bedroom. On her mobile phone.

JENNI: Yes, Sophie, I've been collecting my lunch money so that we can buy some drink. Don't worry I'll get out by Friday. I'll be sweet to me ma. Yes, she's trying to keep me in this week. We've got the damn parents' meeting to go to tonight. Are you going to that? Should be fun, eh? So we all going to that house party on Friday? Should be good.

KATE: Jenni! Come on, it's time to go.

JENNI: Just a minute! *(To Sophie.)* I've gotta go. Later.

JENNI goes into the kitchen.

JENNI: Ok, Ma.

KATE: Are you ready?

JENNI: Yes.

KATE: Right then, let's go.

They put their coats on and put two chairs at the front of the stage to become the school. The following speech is delivered to the audience.

JENNI: The teacher says that my schoolwork has got really bad over the past few months. That I'm not concentrating in class. I'm not going to pass my end-of-term exams at this rate. As if I care.

KATE: The teacher says that her schoolwork has got really bad. That she's not concentrating in class. She's not going to pass her exams at this rate. She asks me if I know why. *(Pause)* I do know why. It's because she's going out on a Thursday and staying out really late all weekend. She's hungover in school. She can barely talk to me until about Tuesday. But I don't say this to the teacher. How can I tell her that? What would she think of me? I say, 'I don't know why, I don't know what's happening.'

JENNI: The teacher asks me if I know why my schoolwork has gone down. *(She shrugs.)* No, dunno, Miss.

KATE: The teacher says it's like she's not there anymore, something is missing. I know what she means.

Put chairs back. Both exit.

SCENE 17

KATE in the kitchen, to audience.
What can I do? You don't want to be too strict. You can't keep them in. But you want to make sure they're safe. I spoke to her father. He said she's just being a 14-year-old and I worry too much. He said he never liked school much either, that she takes after him. I asked him if he would take her for a while. He said he's far too busy.

JENNI tidying her bedroom, to audience.
Me da doesn't want me to stay with him, he's too busy. He's always busy. I wish he was still with us. I suppose he has to work to pay me ma money to look after me. When I was little he used to carry me on his shoulders. I loved that. Being so high up. And he used to play with my

feet and tickle me. My dad's funny, he used to make me laugh. I only see him sometimes now. For my birthday, Christmas, during the holidays. He's not as much fun as he used to be. I wanna go out on Friday. I've got to be nice to me ma. Keep on her good side. That's why I'm cleaning my room. She always likes it when I clean my room. *(She looks around the room, it is tidy now.)* That'll do.

JENNI goes into the kitchen.

JENNI: I've cleaned my room.

KATE *(Surprised)*: Have you? Very good.

JENNI: Yeah, it was getting messy.

KATE: It's been messy for the past six months.

JENNI: I'm sorry about the parents' meeting.

KATE: You have to do something about your schoolwork. If you carry on like that you won't pass any exams. You won't get any qualifications. You won't be able to go to university. You won't get a job. Or you'll end up in some dead-end job that you hate and you'll get paid a pittance for. Is that what you want?

JENNI: No.

KATE: So you have to do better.

JENNI: I'll try harder.

KATE: You used to like school. Especially Art. You're not even doing well in that anymore.

JENNI: I know.

KATE: You need to stop going out so much. Do you know why you can't concentrate in school?

JENNI: Why?

KATE: Because you go out on school nights drinking. You've got a hangover while you're in school and you're tired because you've been up so late. Your body is still growing and you need your sleep.

JENNI: Yeah but you drink and you go to work the next day.

KATE: But I'm not getting drunk. A couple of glasses is ok. I just have them to relax.

JENNI: You do get drunk.

KATE: Ok, sometimes when I go out, which isn't often. And I definitely don't do it when I've got work the next morning because I know I wouldn't be able to do my work.

JENNI: Everybody drinks, Ma, everybody in school. And if you don't keep up with them you're a lightweight. And nobody wants to be called a lightweight.

KATE: Jacob doesn't drink, he seems to manage ok.

JENNI: Yeah but everyone thinks he's weird.

KATE: I know it must be hard when everyone else is doing it but you have to take care of yourself. And you have to keep up with your schoolwork. Or you will have no future.

JENNI: Ok.

KATE: What do want for your tea tonight?

JENNI: Shall we get a takeaway? And a DVD?

KATE: That would be nice. A night in with my wee girl, the way we used to.

JENNI gives KATE a hug.

JENNI: Ma, we have a project to do for school and Sophie said that I could study at her's on Friday. We could study together.

KATE: You're not going out. I've said that already.

JENNI: But it's not going out. I'll be at her house. We won't be going out.

KATE: I don't feel like I can trust you. You've lied to me before.

JENNI: No, really, Ma, I really want to do better at my schoolwork, and so does Sophie, she was telling me. And we want to do well in this project, we are working on it together. Please, Ma.

KATE: What is the project?

JENNI: It's a citizenship project, the world around us.

KATE: Oh, Jenni, I don't know.

JENNI: Please, Ma, I promise, I'll only be at Sophie's, I won't be going out or drinking.

KATE: I'll see.

JENNI: Sweet.

KATE: I'll go and get the menu for the takeaway.

KATE exit.

JENNI *(Triumphant)*: Yes! Yes!

JENNI goes to bedroom. Phones Sophie.

JENNI: Hey, Sophie. We're on for Friday.

SCENE 18

JENNI changes behind screen, speaks to audience.

We start at Sophie's, she has a bottle of vodka. Sophie's house is so big, her ma and da don't know what we get up to. *(Putting make up on.)* What about this colour for my eyes, Sophie? Oh let me try that top on. Does that look good on me? Can I borrow it? Thanks! *(She pulls on a short skirt and puts on high heels.)* Do I look alright? Aw thanks, Sophie, you look like a babe too. We get to the party. There's loads of people there already. The boy's parents are away. It was all over Facebook. Yeah, I'll have a vodka an' orange! It's a big house, massive garden. More and more people coming all the time. There must be about 100. It's getting crazy, music's getting louder. Everyone's dancing, all squashed together.

She dances wildly.

Oh, I feel a bit sick. Where's Sophie? I can't see Sophie. I need to throw up. Make my way to the toilet, there's a queue. Let me in!

She can't get in, she sits on the floor.

OMG I can't hold it anymore.

She throws up.

I hear the voices. I'm lying in my own sick. 'Er… that's disgusting. Look, she's rolling in it.'

I can see the mobile phones, they're all taking photos of me. I want to go home. I want me ma.

I drag myself up. I wanna find Sophie and go home.

She wanders about.

There's Sophie. She's crying. 'Sophie, you alright?' She keeps crying. 'What, Sophie, what's wrong?' She's got mud on her clothes.

Actor plays both parts.

SOPHIE: I was in the garden... *(She sobs.)*

JENNI: Yeah... you were in the garden, and what happened?

SOPHIE: They were... pulling at my clothes... and... touching me... and I couldn't stop them... *(She sobs louder.)*

JENNI: Come on, Sophie, let's go home.

JENNI to audience.
We get out into the street. I want to get a taxi. We start walking. No taxis about. We have to get to a main road. Sophie is still crying. 'Sophie, Sophie, stop crying.' Sophie sees a taxi on the other side of the road. She darts for it, without looking. She walks straight into the road and she is swaying a bit. There's a car coming the other way, it's going really fast. 'Sophie!'

Silence.

The car hits her. She goes flying up into the air. I don't know how high. She comes down on her head. I hear a loud crack. Everything has stood still. There's no sound, or if there is, I can't hear it. I'm frozen, I can't move. I start shaking.

JENNI *(Whispering, shaking.)*: Sophie... Sophie...

She looks like a rag doll. She's not moving. There's a lot of blood. Her leg is twisted in a really random shape.

JENNI: Sophie!

SFX ambulance siren.

SCENE 19

KATE in kitchen, to audience.

Jenni hasn't been out since then. She's had some time off school. The doctor says she's in shock. Sophie was in hospital for four weeks. She's back at home now. Her face was a mess. She is going to be in a wheelchair, they don't know how long for, it could be permanent. I just keep thinking ... *that could've been Jenni*, is that awful? Is that terrible?

A friend told me about this Parenting Teenagers Group that she goes to. I went along. It has really opened my eyes. I didn't realise the fact that I drink was affecting Jenni. I mean, I don't think that I drink a lot, but she has seen me drunk. And I know it was getting worse for a while there.

Every time there was an occasion, any occasion, we would all be drinking, all the children's birthdays. Everybody did it. If you didn't do it, people would think you were strange. If something good happened, you had a drink. If something bad happened, you had a drink. It you just wanted something to do, you had a drink.

In the group they showed us pictures of people drinking when there were children about. There was a picture of a one-year-old's birthday party with the party balloons, the cards, the presents, the crisps, the little sandwiches, sausages on sticks, the plates of sweets. And in amongst it all were the bottles of drink, the cans, the cigarettes. Children playing with empty beer cans. The children altogether, amusing themselves while the grown-ups sat around and drank. I looked at that picture and I recognised it. And it looked disgusting. I was disgusted with myself.

JENNI enters the kitchen.

JENNI: I'm going to go and see Sophie.

KATE: Shall I take you there?

JENNI: No, it's ok.

KATE: Do you need any money?

JENNI: I might buy something to take round.

KATE: Here.

KATE gives her some money.

JENNI: I'll bring back the change.

KATE: Ok.

JENNI: See you later.

KATE: What time?

JENNI: I'll be back by six.

KATE: Ok, see you then.

JENNI: Bye, Ma.

SCENE 20

JENNI to audience.

Sophie looks at me with those eyes that now look so different. I don't know how to talk to her. *(Mimicking herself.)* 'Hi, Sophie, what you up to today? You going to that party that's all over Facebook? What are we bringing to drink? Who do you fancy?' We can't talk like that anymore. I sit down. 'Hi, Sophie, alright?' Of course she's not alright. 'Alright,' she says. She's in her wheelchair. Her face is damaged. They had to do an operation to fix the bones in her face. She has trouble eating food. She needs help going to the toilet. I don't have a friend to go out with anymore. Her mother comes in. 'Hello, Jenni, nice to see you. I'm just going to give Sophie her tea.' She has a plate of something that has been mashed up, and a drink with a straw. She feeds Sophie with a spoon. The phone rings. She tries to answer the phone and feed Sophie at the same time. 'Shall I do that?' She hands me the plate and spoon.

JENNI sits holding the plate and spoon (miming) as if she doesn't know what to do with them. Then she slowly goes to feed Sophie. She wipes some food off of her chin. JENNI starts to cry.

SCENE 21

JENNI at home in her bedroom. Lying on the bed. KATE in kitchen. Silence, KATE looking uneasy. She goes into the bedroom.

KATE: You haven't said anything since you came back. How is Sophie?

JENNI: I was feeding her. I don't think she liked that. They don't know if she will ever be able to walk again. She might always be in a wheelchair.

KATE: She will have to adjust to a new way of doing things. It will take time. People in wheelchairs can do lots of things and they can have as good a life as anyone else.

JENNI: I don't think Sophie thinks that. Oh, Ma, you should see the way she looks at me.

KATE: It will get easier.

JENNI: I'm sorry, Ma.

KATE: Sorry for what?

JENNI: For everything. For all the cheek I was giving to you, for not listening to you, for being out all night and not letting you know where I was. *(She starts crying.)* I'm sorry, Ma.

KATE hugs JENNI.

KATE: Shhh, shhh, shhh. It's ok, darling. I was so scared. When I heard of the accident. I thought it was you. I thought I had lost you. I know that's a terrible thing to say.

JENNI still crying.

JENNI: I won't be like that anymore, Mammy. I promise. I'll let you know where I am. And I'm not going to drink anymore.

KATE: Well you probably will, but not yet, and not down a back lane. Just be careful what you drink and how much. You know, be sensible about it, keep yourself safe.

JENNI: I will, Ma, I will.

KATE: And I will too.

JENNI: What?

KATE: I will be much more careful too. You've seen me and your da drinking all your life. It's no wonder you started. You learned from us. So I am going to try to set a better example. What do you think?

JENNI hugs KATE.

KATE: And when you go out, I'll want to know where you are, what time you will be coming home, and how you are going to get home, ok?

JENNI: Ok.

KATE: Shall we go out for tea? Shall we go for a pizza?

JENNI: Yeah.

KATE: It's good to have my girl back again.

THE END

Lesson/Workshop Plan for *A Wee Taste*

Greta McTague, Head of Drama, St Cecilia's College, Derry

This drama session aims to allow students/participants to:
- Explore the play *A Wee Taste* actively in order to get more out of their experience as audience members.
- Engage with the key themes of the play.

Introduction – Reflections
In a circle, if space permits, ask for adjectives to describe how the group responded to the play, e.g. reflective, hard-hitting, realistic, relatable, interesting, thought-provoking. Invite discussion about how the play relates to young people.

In pairs (while still in the circle), students are invited to rank the following 'Elements and Issues' of the play in terms of how engaging they were for them. (See Resource on page 51, pens/pencils needed.)
- The relationship between Jenni and her mother, Kate
- The friendship between Sophie and Jenni
- The impact of alcohol on Jenni's school life
- The consequences of excessive underage drinking
- The peer pressure to drink alcohol so that one is not considered a 'lightweight'
- How social media can be used in a harmful way

Participants will then feedback the reasons why they felt some aspects of the play were more interesting or important to them than others.

Activity 1 – Walking Debate
This activity is designed to get the group moving in a non-invasive way and to encourage communication.

There are three headings – AGREE, DISAGREE and DON'T KNOW – each of which should be Blu-tacked to a different wall in the same room.

- Everyone stand up

- Explain that everyone must think for themselves and make their own decisions
- Facilitator will point out each of the headings which have been Blu-tacked around the room
- Participants will move to the heading that reflects how they feel about the following statement (facilitator will read this aloud):

Kate is a bad mother with a drink problem.
- Participants will now discuss their opinions
- Participants may change their minds after discussion with other points of view and walk to a different area of the room

Facilitator may want to prompt discussion by asking the following questions or jogging the memories of particular moments in the play:
- Why does Jenni's mother drink?
- What is the difference (if any) between Jenni's drinking and her mother's drinking?
- Can you think of anywhere in the play where Kate makes excuses for drinking?

Five reasons to *disagree* with the statement:
1. Disagree – Kate looks after Jenni and regularly asks her to eat her home-cooked dinners.

2. Disagree – Kate always asks Jenni how she got on at school/ how her day was.

3. Disagree – Kate wants her daughter to work hard at school and be disciplined about homework. (Scene 1: 'Homework first. TV later.')

4. Disagree – Kate regularly expresses concern about who Jenni will be with and when she'll be back when she goes out.

5. Disagree – Kate wants to improve her parenting skills when she joins a Parenting Teenagers Group in Scene 19.

Five reasons to *agree* with the statement:

1. Agree – 'Where is my beautiful, sweet, young girl gone?' Scene 15 – Kate refuses to let her girl move on from childhood and forgets that teenage life can be so difficult for some young people.

2. Agree – Scene 1: Kate doesn't celebrate Jenni's achievement in Art and is dismissive of her brilliant exam result:
   Jenni: I got an A+ in my Art test.
   Kate: That's great, love. Do you know what jobs you can get with Art?
   In Scene 15, when Jenni is no longer working at school because of her drinking, her mother laments:
   'You used to like school. You used to love Art.'
   Jenni replies: 'Yeah, well, like you said yourself, what kind of job could I get with Art?' This shows that Jenni has been discouraged by her mother's earlier remarks.

3. Agree – In Scene 16 at the parent/teacher meeting, Kate is more concerned about what the teacher might think of her as a mother when she pretends that she doesn't know why Jenni's schoolwork is slipping. She should have been honest and explained that her daughter's drinking is out of control.

4. Agree – In Scene 6 Kate allows Jenni to have a sleepover just so that she herself can have a night out with her own friends.

5. Agree – Kate always gives in to Jenni when Jenni asks to go out, even after Kate has told Jenni that she is grounded. Kate is inconsistent and this creates chaos in the house.

Activity 2 – Tableaux of Mother and Daughter
This activity will encourage pupils to mix with others and consider the use of body language to create meaning to tell a story.

Facilitator calls out the following instructions. Be clear and have a sense of urgency to create an energetic atmosphere.
   • Everybody walk. Just walk. Don't talk and don't walk in a circle. Walk by yourself. Don't walk around with your friend.

- Greet each person as you pass – make eye contact, smile and nod – making sure you change direction rather than getting stuck in the pattern of walking in a circle.
- Freeze! Groups of three! Quickly run to the people nearest you to make a group of three. Hold on to them. Don't run to your friends.
- Walk! As before in your individual and random way. Freeze! Groups of five. Quickly and without talking, help to create a group of five. Now make a freeze-frame that represents love – without talking. 10, 9, 8, 7, 6, 5, 4, 3, 2, 1 – time's up!
- Examine each freeze-frame and encourage the whole group to do the same.
- Walk! As before. Groups of three. Now you will stay in this group of three to create a series of five freeze-frames (also called tableaux) to explore how Kate and Jenni's mother/daughter relationship changes from the start to the end of the story.

It is preferable that participants come up with their own five key moments to create their freeze–frames, but the facilitator may suggest the following if necessary:

Suggestions (if necessary) for tableaux (freeze-frames) for Activity 2:

1. Scene 1
   Jenni: I got an A+ in my Art test.
   Kate: That's great, love. Do you know what jobs you can get with Art?

2. Scene 4
   Jenni arrives home and wants to get upstairs before her mother (who is sitting with a glass of wine waiting up for her) asks too many questions. Jenni lies to her mother and says that she didn't text her back because she had no credit.

3. Scene 10
   Jenni is in bed, staying off school after the revealing photos of her were spread around social media. Her mother is concerned, but Jenni won't tell her the real reason why she is staying off school.

4. Scene 11
    Kate finds out why Jenni has been staying off and is very calm but concerned. Jenni seems remorseful and seems to have turned over a new leaf.

5. Scene 14
    Row between Kate and Jenni after the police have taken Jenni home (after Jacob has been assaulted by Rory).

6. Scene 21
    Jenni and Kate are close again after Sophie's terrible accident. Jenni's bravado is gone now and she allows herself to be loved and protected by her mother. Kate is also aware that she can improve herself too.

Each group will perform their freeze-frames. Other group members may suggest ideas to help clarify dramatic intentions in the scene (through suggestions about body language, gesture, facial expressions). Have the freeze-frames changed anyone's perceptions or opinions of the relationship between Kate and Jenni (mother and daughter)? Discuss.

Activity 3 – Conscience Alley for Jacob
This activity will encourage participants to explore Jacob's decision to 'grass' on Rory, who took the revealing photo of Jenni and posted it on social media. 'Conscience Alley' is a useful technique for exploring any kind of dilemma faced by a character, providing an opportunity to analyse a decisive moment in greater detail.

1. The class forms two lines facing each other.
2. One side is asked to think of ways to encourage Jacob to tell the school authorities about what Rory did to Jenni and the other side is asked to think of arguments to persuade Jacob to say nothing about what Rory did to Jenni.
3. One person (the teacher or a participant) takes on the role of Jacob and walks between the lines as each member of the group speaks their advice.
4. 'Jacob' will then discuss with the group how it felt to be faced with the dilemma and this will encourage the group to

consider the issues involved when we have the opportunity to do something about harmful and anti-social behaviour we see around us.

Activity 4 – Off-Text Improvisation

This technique will encourage participants to explore how we use social media without fully taking into account how our choices might impact on the lives of others.

In Scene 10 Jenni finds out that Rory has sent revealing photos of her around social media and that these pics have been shared widely.

1. In pairs, participants will improvise a short scene where two young people are discussing the pictures of Jenni drunk and topless, which have been shared around social media. They also decide to share the images.
2. Run the scene again, but this time Jenni walks into the room where the two young people are discussing the issue.
- How does Jenni's presence change the behaviour of the two young people?
- Do they talk to her?
- Do they feel any differently about sharing the pictures after they have communicated with Jenni?
- Do they avoid her and pretend that nothing's happening?

Explain that if you share an indecent image of someone then you are complicit in the crime and could face charges of sending indecent images of children online.

Discussion point: Has social media brought us closer to one another or are we somehow more detached from one another? Is our social experience richer and deeper, or more shallow and artificial?

Activity 5 – Peer Group Pressure – Role Play

This activity will encourage participants to think about how they might help someone who is starting to 'go off the rails' and raises awareness of the various agencies in the city that can help young people in crisis. Read the following to the whole group and discuss.

- Someone younger than you is being influenced too strongly by a friend to engage in underage drinking and risky behaviour. What would your advice be?

  Points you might consider:
  - ✓ Trusting your own opinions
  - ✓ The desire to be the same as everyone else
  - ✓ Coping with rejection
  - ✓ Standing up for yourself
  - ✓ Where can you go for further help? Ask the participants first before you suggest some of the following: Samaritans, HURT, Zest, Nexus, Childline, Bogside and Brandywell Health Forum, School Counsellor.

- In pairs, improvise a scene between two young people where one is expressing concern about the other's underage drinking. Use the points for consideration above to help you.

- After this activity, do you feel you would be more confident about speaking to someone you were concerned about if they were involved in underage drinking?

- Do you feel more confident about saying no to people who may try to persuade you to drink alcohol or take illegal substances?

Conclusion
Form a circle. In turn, each person will come to the middle, reach out an arm and offer one word/phrase to describe how s/he felt about the session or what s/he will take from the session.

Counting Down
The aim of this final calming activity is to mark an ending of the drama session. Students are asked to count backwards from 10 to 1 with their eyes closed. While doing so, they should reduce the volume of their voices. Number 10 is spoken out loudly whereas the following numbers are spoken out with decreasing volume. Finally, number 1 should only be whispered.

Resource – Introduction: Reflections

Discuss with your partner which parts of the play were the most interesting for you. In pairs, rank in order (1-6) how interesting each of the 'Elements and Issues' are to you after seeing/reading the play, with 1 being the most interesting.

Number _____	Number _____
Elements and Issues The relationship between Jenni and her mother, Kate.	**Elements and Issues** The friendship between Sophie and Jenni.
Number _____	Number _____
Elements and Issues The impact of alcohol on Jenni's school life.	**Elements and Issues** The consequences of excessive underage drinking (what can happen when you drink too much).
Number _____	Number _____
Elements and Issues The peer pressure to drink alcohol so that you're not considered a 'lightweight'.	**Elements and Issues** How social media can be used in a harmful way.

About the Author

Patricia Byrne is a Writer, Director and Producer living in Derry since 1993. She is the Artistic Director and Co-Founder of Sole Purpose Productions which was set up in 1997 to investigate and illuminate social and public issues through the discourse of theatre.

She has written seven plays for Sole Purpose which have toured all over Ireland and the UK. *Don't Say A Word* toured for ten years and was nominated for an Amnesty International Freedom of Expression Award at the Edinburgh Fringe Festival in 2008. It toured Scotland in 2009 when it was performed in the Scottish Parliament at the invitation of the Cross-Party Group on Men's Violence Against Women and Children.

See No Evil, a play which portrays a situation of elder abuse in rural Ireland and first produced in 2008, was adapted in 2016 by Sken:nen A'Onsonton, an organisation that works with First Nations people on the Kahnawake Reservation in Quebec, Canada. The play was adapted with their elders as part of their Alternative Dispute Resolution Programme.

Patricia wrote and produced *Blinkered* in 2016, a play which explores issues around mental health and suicide in young people. In 2017 she was invited to Roosevelt High School in Seattle, USA, to work with students on the issues explored in *Blinkered*. Supported by the Arts Council of Northern Ireland Artists International Development Fund, she worked with students to develop 'Scenes of Intervention', a series of short drama scenes which looked at ways to talk about suicide. These scenes were presented at a Youth Mental Health Awareness Event in Seattle in May 2017.

In her work as a Producer and Director she has developed many productions with the LGBT community and received the Noel Walsh Freedom Award in 2012 and the Helen Harris Freedom Award in 2014 for making a significant contribution to LGBT rights and furthering the equality agenda.

Patricia is working on a new theatre piece entitled *Samara's Shop* which explores issues of immigration and refugees through the ages.

Other Plays by the Author

Plays in this series
Don't Say A Word
See No Evil
Every Move You Make

Other plays
Under The Carpet: Explores a situation of sexual abuse within the family. It was first produced in 2001.

Snow White – The Remix: A feminist fairy tale for all the family. It was first produced in 2002, with remounts in 2006 and 2008.

Blinkered: Explores the issues of mental health and suicide. It was first produced in 2016 and toured again in 2017.

All plays are available from Sole Purpose Productions.